Also by Gilbert Sorrentino

PROSE

The Sky Changes
Steelwork
Imaginative Qualities of Actual Things
Splendide-Hôtel

VERSE

The Darkness Surrounds Us
Black and White
The Perfect Fiction
Corrosive Sublimate

Gilbert Sorrentino

FLAWLESS PLAY RESTORED

THE MASQUE OF FUNGO

BLACK SPARROW PRESS • LOS ANGELES • 1974

 For information address Black Sparrow Press, P.O. Box 25603, Los Angeles, CA, 90025.

LIBRARY OF CONGRESS CATALOGING IN PUBLICATION DATA

Sorrentino, Gilbert.
Flawless play restored : the masque of Fungo.

Part of a novel-in-progress presented in play form, but not intended for the stage.
I. Title.
PS3569.07F5 812'.5'4 74-22436
ISBN 0-87685-198-7
ISBN 0-87685-197-9 pbk.

CHARACTERS

SUSAN B. ANTHONY, a Massachusetts belle of some balls
JACK ARMSTRONG, one-time religious maniac, now an ROTC ensign from a good home
BARNACLE BILL, a sailor
EDDY BESHARY, an Arabian etymologist
ROBERTO BLIGH, a bard of the Vast Heartland
ALICE BLUEGOWN, a small-town virgin, her cheeks suffused with crimson
PETER BOFFO, iconoclastic editor of *Lamplighter Views*
BROTHER OF SAL RONGO, Sal Rongo's brother
LANCE DELRIO, a man about small Southwestern towns
DUCHESS, an erotically unhinged noblewoman
FAIR YOUNG MAIDEN, an innocent lass in cotton underwear
FOOTS FUNGO, a star shortstop who's lost a step
FUCKING WHORE, a girl with a past
ODILE GASHE, a tribade in sensible shoes
HARRY THE CRAB, a hairy wonder
"POP" HEART, wily editor of the *Belleville Vetch*
HURLEY LEES, a bogeyman of obscure Celtic origins
JIM JAM, a romantic loser, suitably accoutered
JAMES JOYCE, a grocer's assistant
"SHOTGUN" JAREMA, manager of the Amarillo Centipedes
KID SISTER, a kid sister
MICHAEL "MILKY" KIDWELL, a retired General, "the Hero of Pusan"
PADDY DOWN KILLARNEY, a thick Irish cop
SEAN ALEXANDER KURKJIAN, a concrete poet
BILLY McCOY, a musical boy
FATHER DANNY MAVOURNEEN, a disgraced priest who lives among the People

MINUSCULE FIGURE OF TY COBB, a small miracle
ABRAHAM NESBIT, D.D.S., a fake dentist
MONSIGNOR BERNARD O'HARA, a North of Ireland convert with eccentric leanings
OLD JOE, a disease
VINNIE PACHISI, a loudmouthed thug
SIGNORINA RIGATONI, a blazing-eyed gypsy lass
RITA RIGHT, a sensitive poetess from Omaha
SAL RONGO, a remarkably stupid delicatessen customer
CLARK SITZ, a mysterious bather
MARQUIS DE SADE, a disturbed nobleman who cannot relate
BETSY JEAN DAISY SMITH, one-time Miss Algebra and now the Senator's secretary
AIRMAN SMITH, Betsy Jean's husband
ELEAZAR SOD, Ph.D., a Guggenheim Fellow
SPIRIT OF CARMEN CAVALLARO, a ghost of a chance
SENATOR STREET, a depraved legislator
TINKER, a loathsome fellow from Australia
WANTON NYMPH, a Continental vamp
CHARLES DEXTER WARD, a dupe of the Communists
WUN EM EN, a brilliant young book editor of Oriental birth
"CRACKER" YALOBUSHA, manager of the Biloxi Crips

Plus Ant'ny, Audience, Bands, Blackstone, Certain Frenchmen, Chair, Discarded Wiener, Effort, God, Hope of the Future, Italo-American Toughs, Rumor, Sin of Onan, Small Group of Wealthy Texans, Thousands of American Boys, Unbelievable Pressures, USO, Villistas, Voice of Satan, White-Robed Choir, Masquers, and others.

Flawless Play Restored

The scene is a major-league ball park, the home of a team of disconcerting ineptitude. It is so devised as to seem to be floating uncomfortably in a surrounding sea of parking lots, subway tracks and trestles, highways, and vast areas of bogland. There is a strong possibility that the landscape represents New Jersey. At each position on the field stands a Masquer, dressed in garments of dull flame color, surrounded by massy clouds out of which each seems to be unsuccessfully peering. They fidget with their ill-fitting sunglasses. On the backs of their darkly fiery costumes, above their numbers, are their names, those of the nine elements of Ugliness. There are the pitcher, DULLNESS, the catcher, MURKINESS, the first baseman, DETERIO-RATION, the second baseman, UNHAPPINESS, the third baseman, IMMODERATION, the shortstop, HOMELINESS, the left fielder, WORTHLESSNESS, the center fielder, IMPERFECTION, and the right fielder, DISHARMONY. Standing off to the right of the first-base foul line is a figure dressed like all the others. He is completely enveloped in clouds which occasionally break to reveal his name, dimly discernible through the swirling mists. It is clear that he is made up of all the other elements, being HOPE-LESSNESS. The Masquers suddenly move from their positions and enter, in a straggling fashion, the dugout, where they sing this song:

On the brave field of playe,
    Tu-whit, tu-whoo, jug-jug
    And ding-a-ding,
The player *Fungo* did his errors make
    Thirty-eighte by May.

What in the name of *Jesu*
    Is he doing?
    Jug! shouted each lustie fan.
Not onlie are his fingres wooden
But he's hitting .002.

But folke, observe our presentacioun
    Of brave heroicks
    And of faith and workes

Fungo shall engage his fate
To your delectacioun.

During this musical presentation, the stage has slowly revolved away from the audience so that by the song's termination, the Masquers are completely hidden, and the stage seems to be bare. The lights intensify to reveal it cluttered with various characters.

SUSAN B. ANTHONY

I long for a multiple clitoral orgasm without the intercession of the usual bore of a male organ! I long! I long!

(*She is carried off, her pelvis convulsing in time to the old Feltman's favorite, "I'd Press My Thighs Together Ere I'd Kiss Your Greedy Lips."*)

BILLY McCOY

If thy rod offend thee, pluck it!

(*He commits the Sin of Onan.*)

THE SIN OF ONAN

(*being dragged to a mental hospital*)

I'm as sane as you are!

SUSAN B. ANTHONY

(*her homely hands lost 'neath the severe folds of her chaste tweed skirt*)

I feel like the dark-haired beauty in that "certain" French daguerrotype! A wanton nymph! Wheee!

WANTON NYMPH

Oh là!

(*She rushes across the room, trips, and flies through the air.*)

Ze hell weez your theeng! Weel zom wan pleez get me off ze doorknob?

(*Blushes.*)

JAMES JOYCE

Look to the lady.

FOOTS FUNGO

It took a bad hop! It took a real bad hop!

(*He kicks at the keystone sack and breaks a toe.*)

OFFICER KILLARNEY

(*chewing a homemade cross of blessèd palm*)

Is it the traffic ye think ye'll be blockin' wit yer dirthy commie bodies?

(*Begins beating nuns, Methodist clergymen, babies, cripples, old Jews, tricycles, artists manqués, homosexual gentlemen, well-bred ladies, Fellows of Reconciliation, liberal schoolteachers, and many others.*)

GENERAL KIDWELL

There is indeed a glimmer, a faint ray, of light at the end of the long tunnel of permissive American softness. Such men as this belovèd Irish patrolman will see to it.

(*He soils his officer's pinks.*)

SUSAN B. ANTHONY

(*gently placing a satchel charge into Kidwell's beribboned blouse*)

You do go on, General!

(*aside*)

I hate to say it, but that's what I call a *man*.

JAMES JOYCE

I call that a scumhead.

CLARK SITZ

(*bathing resignedly*)

Now for a brisk towel-down.

CHARLES DEXTER WARD

The carrots are growing up through the snows of Siberia! The great submarine flotilla of the People's Navy is about to sail for Odessa! Have none of you the sanity to understand what this means for mankind? Kidwell, your blouse is oddly lumpy.

GENERAL KIDWELL

(*blowing up*)

Pass in review! You're to report to your C.O., Miss Anthony, for company punishment. I think you've broken a medal.

SUSAN B. ANTHONY

(*turning into Lydia Pinkham, a crazed pharmacist*)

At last! Now I won't have to miss all the fun! Freedom from cramps and odor on those "certain" days.

(*She plunges through some nearby ice and swims about underwater in a carefree manner.*)

I can swim again! No more playing at the gauche game of "beach wallflower" for me.

DUCHESS

(*dressing for a ball*)

I know I should be frightfully ashamed of myself but I cawn't help spying on that tinker's remarkable kidney wiper.

(*A bejeweled hand disappears 'neath the lacy folds of her rich petticoat.*)

TINKER

(*pissing up against a wall*)

Gor blimey! This 'ere bloody Duchess is spyin' on me flamin' kidney wiper, she is, and 'at's no bloody lie!

DR. ELEAZAR SOD

The tensile strength of these Belgian blown-glass decanters of the period 1863 to 1866 may well be . . .

RITA RIGHT

Hello, you Fellow!

TINKER

(*shamelessly polluting himself*)

Bloody sod!

HARRY THE CRAB

When suddenly confronted by a pigeon crushed to the pavement —YOU MUST EAT IT! Arrgghhh, God! My pimples, my boils!

(*He scratches all over and ends by clawing feverishly at his grey fedora, which item too is covered by a repulsive growth.*)

What dog will bite me today? Woe! Woe!

(*His nose begins to bleed onto his fedora.*)

ALL sing:

Who has heard tell of Crab, the corrupt
Also yclept "the Hairy"?
How on a morning his skin did erupt
The sight did make men wary.
His hirsute frame, his swinish odor
Enough to make all flee
All heightened by his weird fedora

Such none did ever see.

Here's to Harry, the Hairy Wonder!
God bless him, hat and all.
Bless his pimples, bless his boils
And bless his ruptured ball!

Within his slouched and wondrous hat
There drums a constant headache,
His mouth felt oft like a welcome mat
Beneath his painful nosebreak.
What availed high thoughts of art or craft?—
His ass did hideously quake!
He might as well be dumb or daft
His life is not too jake.

Yet! Here's to Harry, the Hairy Wonder! *etc.*

SUSAN B. ANTHONY

(*gazing at a drawing of Dixie Dugan in her frillies*)

Is it true what they say about Dixie?

(*She unsuccessfully attempts to ravish the newspaper.*)

RITA RIGHT

Oh come to me not
As chestnut blossoms ope
Upon my carmine lips, sobbing
Heart in thrall, Oh come not . . . .

JAMES JOYCE

A washable floatable lovable doll.

AUDIENCE

Sing "Sorrento"!
Sing "Mama"!
Sing "I Met Maria in the Pasticceria"!

(*They begin to toy with their gold earrings and to twirl*

their mustaches.)

Do the fuckin' Harlem Glide!

BILLY McCOY

(*playing that old pianna on the steamship "Alabama"*)

Note well how each fish and worm begins to twist and squirm!

A White-Robed Choir, including Dan Lop, Roche Mongan, Peter Cloran, Tom Treacle, Christopher Leming-Hoptt, L.M. Churl, John O. Nose, J.H. Rome, Clete Banjo, Joe H. Snart, Maj. Rumford Rug, Charles E. Chin, Pinafore Jaizus, Mary N. Joseph, Pablo Tortuga, Paulo Turrone-Tortilla, Carmela Vanella, Gibson Martini, Count Monte Crisco, Harrison Carter, et. al., *enters, and accompanied by McCOY, sings a medley of old favorites. They are:* I Won't Steal Your Wafers; That Dear Old Jar of Vaseline; Skunk Cabbage, Starlight, and You; Gas, We Gave No Enémas; Your Expensive Spread Bewitches Me; Sixty-nine in Old Caroline; My Bowling Ball Has Fallen to the Floor; I'm P-Polish and P-Proud of It; Your Sweet Soiled Nightgown in the Moonlight; My Cazz' Has Got the Hots for Only You; Marmalade and Mary in the Mornin'; The Quaint Old Catamite; We're Gonna Blow the Dikes Tonight; Gee, I Miss Those Arizona Sandstorms; Lost in Lou'siana With Lewd Lou; You're My Migraine Headache, You; Jeeter Put Saltpetre in My Greens; In the Waiting-Room of Your Desire; That Dear Old Credenza of Mine; Don't Sella! Your Swella! Umbrella!; Silver Hairs Upon the Chifferobe; In Hackettstown They Let Their Plackets Down For Me; The Glass Streets of Tarrytown; Candlelight Upon Your Stye; The Night the Flowered Sofa Fell On Dad; I'm Climbing Through the Window of Your Heart; There's a Small Focacceria in Your Eyes; A Onion and You; In the Confessional With Bill; Hail, Holy Queen; My Puella Loves Her Fella; Down in Sunny Dade We Call a Spade a Spade; My Love is

Trembling on the Sheer Edge of the Meaningless; Let Me Share My Chocolate Chip With You; I Love Ya, Bibelot Belle; A Mets Cap, Rose Hips, and You; Eat My Chowder; *and* A Jig in a Wig.

SENATOR STREET

I say that nuking the Reds would be a courageous act of Christian charity, belovèd by every cracker of whatever race, creed, or color in this Great Nation! Think of the Thousands of American Boys who'd be saved! To fight another day! Even spicks on welfare might make it!

THOUSANDS OF AMERICAN BOYS

Get the troops outta the fuckin' sun!

MONSIGNOR O'HARA

Our prayers go out to those Thousands of American Boys. Clapped up or not, they are God's own.

(*He prays.*)

JAMES JOYCE

There's nothing like a new cure for an old clap.

BARNACLE BILL

Open the door and lay on the floor!

FAIR YOUNG MAIDEN

Do I detect a bestial bulge in Sailor Bill's blue bells?

ODILE GASHE

(*absently fingering her crewcut*)

If you'd worn sensible shoes this brutish mariner might have ignored you . . .

BARNACLE BILL

I'll brutish you, by thunderation! I'll keelhaul yer mizzen!

(*He does so to Sapphic protest.*)

OFFICER KILLARNEY

(*arresting an Ejaculation*)

Come wi' me now, ye little spalpeen. Shure, an' it's dirthying the public streets ye'd be up to, eh?

(*He scratches his head and steals an apple from a laughing Italian fruitstand that appears as if by magic.*)

CLARK SITZ

(*endeavoring to avert his gaze from the sylphlike image of Dixie Dugan, still in her unmentionables*)

When all else fails a cool hip bath may assist the young man in tempering the flames of desire that threaten to boin him all up!

(*He begins bathing again.*)

JAMES JOYCE

Divine views from back to the front.

HARRY THE CRAB

Would it help my varied pimples, carbuncles, and boils?

(*A large dog begins savaging one of his suppurating ankles.*)

Why is it that when I waken I am invariably covered with hair? I'll write to Henry Miller! Wise Hank knows much of the unruly fletch!

(*He sings "The Lament of Harry the Crab," or "The Parvenu of Second Avenue":*)

I am Harry, the Wandering Jew
With piles and psoriasis,
Eczema too.
Whatever affliction may be about

Ruptured anuses, measles, gout,
Chicken pox, mumps, or the Asian flu:
I got it—plus dogshit on my shoe!

Harry they call me: dirty guy!
With an itching crotch and a
Wide-open fly.
Whenever a lunger coughs and spits
Whenever a mongrel pisses and shits
I get some in the throat or eye!
It's the poet's cross, I sigh.

Nom de plume of Harry the Crab
I can't, in blizzard or flood,
Get a cab.
The hackies chortle and pass me up
Splash me with mud like a mangy pup
Gas pains in my colon lance and stab—
I'm God's gift to the pharmaceutical lab.

I'm Hairy Harry, the wondrously sick!
Eating pigeons in the park,
I misplaced my dick.
Searching for it in the grass
I found I'd also lost my ass!
Stung to what is left of my quick
I cursed God: who hit me with a brick!

Thus Harry the Crab, the Sick, the Hairy,
Sans pee-pee and of ass devoid;
Has nothing left for Sue or Mary,
And homeless is his hemorrhoid.

EDDY BESHARY

Must I forever stand in the laundry room of life endeavoring to refresh my somewhat exhausted spirits with a glass of Hires root beer and a Camel cigarette?

SIGNORINA RIGATONI

Zom'body do me, no? Oo wan's do me?

(*Her limbs casually fly akimbo.*)

JACK ARMSTRONG

(*trying bravely to peer from beneath his glist'ring visor*)

I'll take a chance, ma'm. Back in Belleville, Illinois, I was known as Jack the Joint, a religious fan!

"POP" HEART

(*misty-eyed*)

Jack was destined for a certain fame. The only man in Southern Illinois who was born without an ass!

(*He sets type.*)

FUCKING WHORE

If I had only kept up my ballet and clarinet lessons I wouldn't be this fucking whore who now stands shamefully before you.

(*She sobs as someone shows her a still from* The Red Shoes.)

Oh, Jesus! Art, beautiful art!

(*She does a split.*)

SENATOR STREET

(*discovered raising his secretary's skirt*)

I have said it before and I say it again—there is nothing wrong with giving a talented young woman a little assistance in the jungle that is Washington.

(*He massages, as if by accident, his pelvic area with the hem of the young woman's skirt.*)

BETSY JEAN DAISY SMITH

Why, Senator Street! What would my husband, a far-flung Airman Second-Class, think of this?

(She emits a modest groan as her skirt trembles.)

Here a bluish cloud appears, high above the am'rous scene. It sparkles with a myriad lights, which on closer inspection are revealed to be various military medals, medallions, insignia, and ornaments, each dazzling, winking, and blinking patriotically as the cloud, being constructed on the order of machina versatilis, *turns about to reveal, seated in its fluffy azure center, his blue uniform this color's perfect complement, AIRMAN SMITH, who seems somewhat bemused, albeit comfy, as befits a military man.*

AIRMAN SMITH

I can thank the Red Cross for this visit home or wherever I am. Hello! Was that Betsy Jean's groan I saw?

(Searches frantically through his cloud.)

SENATOR STREET

Sweet—Jesus—H.—Christ!!

(He more or less comes.)

BETSY JEAN DAISY SMITH

Do that thing, hoss!

(She helps him along in her efficient secretarial way.)

JAMES JOYCE

All the world loves a big gleaming jelly.

AIRMAN SMITH

That *is* Betsy Jean. Now I know why I was flung so far!

(He turns into a Jew Communist.)

A band of Orientals of indeterminate origin enters. They play upon a thousand twangling instruments.

JAMES JOYCE

(*musing*)

Where could Shakespeare have heard a German band?

PETER BOFFO

(*seated once again resignedly before his lonely sheet of white paper*)

We do not like to hear inferior work by superior people . . . .

SEAN ALEXANDER KURKJIAN

bark crab
crab bark
bark bark
crab crab

yayay!

sisisisis

JIM JAM

(*eating his trench coat*)

The man has reified the concept of the crabbèd bark! Of the rousing cheer! Of the kid sister!

KID SISTER

You wouldn't send a sight like me up on a skid like that on a date like this?

WUN EM EN

It's easy to see that he's interested in the possibilities of the language, folks! A marvelous addition to our prestige list.

CHARLES DEXTER WARD

Is there no pity left anywhere in the world for Alger Hiss? For his hidden back issues of *The Nation*? For his eyes of blue, his kisses too? There is a possibility, so rumor has it, that he now reads nothing but signs.

RUMOR

I HAVE IT!

FOOTS FUNGO

If I could play every day I'd break outta this slump. I have a lotta trouble with the breaking ball . . . and have to play every day to . . .

WUN EM EN

We cannot, unfortunately, see our way clear to allowing you to play every day at the present time. However, we'd very much like to see more of your work.

SUSAN B. ANTHONY

Your sexism is the more reprehensible because it is unconscious. I cannot believe that you were unaware that Fungo is a morphodite.

ALICE BLUEGOWN

De sweed sdrains of de drumpet flood drough de sygamores like gleamink candlelighd. Ah, I feel faind!

(*She is suddenly felled by an acute seizure of partheno-genesis.*)

JAMES JOYCE

It was I egged her on to the Stork Exchange and lent my dutiful face to her customs.

SEAN ALEXANDER KURKJIAN

My head is red.

WANTON NYMPH

I fear 'twas ze door, how you say knob, zat creeped in m'lady's plackets, as she creep eento mine, no?

JAMES JOYCE

You can tell by their extraordinary clothes.

FATHER MAVOURNEEN

Miss Bluegown is my good friend and nothing more. I have nothing more to say.

(*Clanking chains are heard.*)

What dark magic has conjured up the demon, Hurley Lees?

(*Sings:*)

Hurley Lees, come blow your horn,
The king's son is in your garden.
Hurley Lees, September morn,
Each Baptist begs your pardon.

Kindly take your chains away
Let each roller shout and pray
E'en rain can come another day
So why break hump?

Hurley Lees, please shove your horn
And have a Bushmills whisky.
In the meadows rich with corn
Ravish Barbara Friskie.

Do not burden honest folk
With cold steel and heavy yoke
We praise each lousy Celtic joke
So why break hump?

HURLEY LEES

(*clanking, etc.*)

The king's son is in my garden! Ravish Barbara Friskie, eh?

(*Blows his horn.*)

To hell with the Protestants!

(*He defiles a Methodist church.*)

EDDY BESHARY

(*vocally imitating a snappy banjo break*)

How excellent to witness Mr. Lees sedulously and assiduously playing upon his primitive instrument! Clearly he is diligent in his intent to move up to the penthouse whose fabled visage is turned toward the myriads of planets, comets, nebulars, galaxies, and shivering starries.

FOOTS FUNGO

Anyone can make three errors in a row. These things all even out over the season.

(*He begins to cry and protest as the team bus of the Amarillo Centipedes pulls up.*)

JAMES JOYCE

You is feeling like you was lost in the bush, boy?

LANCE DELRIO

A few weeks o' that good ole, hot ole chili an' you'll be goin' into the hole an' makin' that good throw.

(*He turns into Anthony Quinn and begins to consume his sweaty, calloused fingers.*)

OFFICER KILLARNEY

The fawkin' greaser kin talk good American, by Christ!

JACK ARMSTRONG

His dark secret Latin blood stands him in good stead, the old artificial.

(*He goes down with his ship.*)

CLARK SITZ

(*running another tub*)

That's cooling the old ardor!

FUCKING WHORE

And yet . . . DelRio was so essentially innocent, so natural in his perverse sexuality. We might have met, once.

(*Her heart turns into gold.*)

SUSAN B. ANTHONY

At home, she launders and dusts. In the office, she is a patronized slave to the typewriter, the filing cabinet, and the coarse jokes of her leering bosses. At play, she must lose gracefully. In bed, she must pretend an ecstasy she neither feels nor comprehends. In her intellectual life, she must display a charming stupidity. In all the aspects of her benighted existence, she is a very nigger, a jigaboo, a boot and a woogie. One might go so far as to call her a nonpromotable. Is it any wonder that Fate has destined her to be this fucking whore?

AUDIENCE

Sing "Oh, Marie," you fuckin' puttan'!

(*They eat large caponato sandwiches and exude giant waves of ethnic warmth.*)

Hey, wotta pair o' tits on that broad!
Hey baby, trow some up here!

They continue to act disgracefully. As their behavior becomes more horrifying, the entire scene opens to reveal the old Fabian Fox Theater, newly decorated in trappings and hangings of Teaneck Red and Bath Beach Gold. Thousands of French-toed alligator shoes tap out the nostalgic rhythms of "Angelina" to brimming eyes and sodden cheeks. Suddenly, on the gleaming stage, the champion fox-trot team of Yo and Patsy appears, dancing nimbly and joyously through the intricate steps that triumphantly took them to the Harvest Moon Ball finals. Just as the old tune reaches a crescendo, the scene disappears even more suddenly than it came into view, and in the ensuing silence, there is only the voice of:

FUCKING WHORE

I too could have been a great dancer had Fate not given me an overwhelming curiosity concerning the ways of Eros. To me, each erection, like the rosy dawn, is new! There is something marvelous about them. They are like—like the sea off Riis Park!

AUDIENCE

'Ey! Trow the fuckin' whore out!
Wot kinda fuckin' language is that?
I got my mudder's pitcher in my wallet!

(*From the midst of the gay crowd comes a shower of peppers, escarole, zucchini, eggplants, and other lusty foodstuffs.*)

WUN EM EN

Perhaps the reading public is ready for an in-depth yet popular study of the ways of these quaint and irrepressible folk.

SENATOR STREET

I abhor and condemn this violence!

(*Mother Cabrini hits him with a store-front Social Club.*)

BETSY JEAN DAISY SMITH

It was an old eyetalian lady who attacked you, sugar!

CLARK SITZ

(*peering at Betsy Jean's limbs*)

Bath . . . bath . . . cool . . . ooohhh . . .

MONSIGNOR O'HARA

Call upon the Name of the Holy Family when temptation accosts you, my son. The Church knows that even Protestants, despite their ice-cream parades, can be tempted. Miss Smith is clearly Satan in short skirts.

(*aside*)

Quite lovely skirts, too. Hmmm. I wonder if she bought that little number off the rack?

CLARK SITZ

JESUS, MARY, AND JOSEPH!

(*He eats the soap.*)

HARRY THE CRAB

Ordinarily, Satan sprinkles my skin with loathsome carbuncles when I have been impure. Woe, woe!

(*His fedora decays.*)

DR. ELEAZAR SOD

In Latvia, *circa* 1889, there was a sudden outbreak of decaying fedoras. I have of late written a monograph on the phenomenon.

LANCE DELRIO

Would I steal money from a friend's overcoat? Would I rape his wife on Christmas Eve while he's away at the funny farm? Would I sit around his house all day while he works at a punch press, eating his food, drinking his beer, and porking his devoted mate? Would I starve his cat and smash his bathroom door, read his letters and write in the margins of his books? Would I steal his pen? What do you take me for? Am I a no-count greaser from the border? I am a greengo in my heart, man!

CHARLES DEXTER WARD

This unfortunate young man is clearly the product of a diet of comic books, refried beans, cold coffee, and sheepshearing. In short, an unfortunate greaseball. Are not our Mexican brothers to be allowed the sweets of the fruits of the riches of the earth?

A ragged mariachi band enters. They sing and play.

Oh in mi cafetal
Mi hat ees on de wall
Mi corazón ees small
So are mi beans!

Seek out mi gleaming head
'Neath habichuelas red
Jou'll find me brain is fled
Eat op mi beans!

That ees why I sing, O!
Mi cafetal ees blue,
Hear the church bell ring, O!
It's ting-a-ling for jou,
Underneath the bush, O!
A Mexicali Rose
She love cornmeal mush, O!
I kiss her op her nose.

In mi machismo pride
Lies mi arthritic side
But passion long denied
(*bis*) Burns op mi beans.

SMALL GROUP OF WEALTHY TEXANS

Good ol' boys! They good ol' boys!

(*They shuffle around, pretending to eat some cold tortillas, and say "muchachos."*)

JACK ARMSTRONG

(*surfacing*)

Lance is all heart in my book. Who can forget him as an NCO? Who cannot remember the day he threw the kitten out the barracks window? A soldier! Is not a man subject to all those temptations and so on?

LANCE DELRIO

Despite all, my heart is a rhapsody in blue, as is my swarthy flesh.

HARRY THE CRAB

That's *fletch*!

(*He is momentarily resplendent in wispy mustache.*)

SUSAN B. ANTHONY

(*seized by a nameless remorse*)

Comrade consciousness-raising feminist group leader, here are my monthly dues.

(*She has a wet dream.*)

ODILE GASHE

Those homespun tweeds take forever to dry, Miz Anthony. Care to slip into something more comfortable?

(*She discreetly straps on a large pink latex dildo.*)

SIGNORINA RIGATONI

Blefu tozd kapozh kapozhchn Estonie!

(*She hastily turns away but not before the tiny golden cross at her throat begins to disintegrate.*)

DR. NESBIT

Even I'd like a taste of that!

(*He drills and extracts indiscriminately.*)

ALICE BLUEGOWN

De nodes of de drumpet sdill gome sweedly to my ears. How gan you be so blint to beaudy?

(*She gives off an exquisite odor of patchouli.*)

FOOTS FUNGO

I think I've been droppin' my hands on the pitch.

WUN EM EN

We've followed you up many a blind alley, Fungo.

FUNGO is bundled into the Centipedes' bus.

I'm afraid it's cheeseburgers, Cokes, and country music from now on for you.

FUNGO is handed a 5 x 7 glossy photo of Bobby Richardson at prayer.

"SHOTGUN" JAREMA

Y'all run out every grounder on this club, boy!

The bus leaves for Wichita Falls and a five-game series with the red-hot Sunstrokes.

TINKER

(*performing atop the panting DUCHESS*)

A bloody fookin' game for girls!

DUCHESS

Oh, you sweaty, smelly, wonderful beast!

(*Runs pop in the thrilling black silk stockings that encase her lovely limbs like a smooth second skin.*)

SEAN ALEXANDER KURKJIAN

His head is red.

WANTON NYMPH

Eet had bettair come out wiz ze nombair on eet or ze Duke weel be piqued.

(*She dies laughing at the memory of this chestnut.*)

FUCKING WHORE

Such repressed sexual attitudes are eroding the very fiber of the nation! My first love preferred his handkerchief to my uh-uh and now he is little more than a Chinese laundryman!

(*She stands straight and proud in her proud free nakedness.*)

There must be no restrictions on complete sexual expression. I stand before you as a horrible example of pre-adolescent misinformation.

MARQUIS DE SADE

The lady has the right idea.

(*His cold crystal-blue eyes glitter as he fashions a little noose.*)

Freedom from all oppression!

By means of the swift and expert maneuvering of a scena ductilis, *we are instantly in the presence of a large and enthusiastic political meeting of a persuasion. The Masquers, still clad in their resplendent costumes, are paired, two by two, with ten of the most lissome, winsome, and appetizing of maids, both male and female, their youthful bodies fetchingly adorned with scraps and patches of star-spangled bunting. The entire group of twenty, shifting beautifully and in a quiet yet pronounced rhythm, forms, in rapid succession, the following motifs: a large cherry bomb; an oil portrait of Henry Ford by Diego Rivera; Ho Chi Minh's Salem cigarette; a menu autographed by an intelligent book reviewer; a pitcher of lemonade; the Liberty Bell; Kansas; a front porch; a runaway slave; a Jewish noncom; an open fire hydrant; an all-right guy, a groovy cat and a great chick; a thoughtful Hollywood star; a gay fascist; and the Polo Grounds. As suddenly as these tableaux have appeared, the entire scene vanishes, so swiftly that one might think it was never there at all. In its place, a giant picture of Justine is seen, dominating the stage; she is partially undressed and is chewing on a gold-knobbed cane with some discretion. Great crystal tears, magically lighted from the inside by means of torches held by Terrific Young People, course down her cheeks. Pinned to her tattered chemise is a button on which is inscribed a motto attributed to D.A.F. de Sade: "IF IT FEELS GOOD DO IT TO OTHERS." The scene disappears into a blue Miami evening, one of many.*

GENERAL KIDWELL

I have it on good authority that it was Miss Whore who clapped up the sleepy little burg of Blackstone, Virginia, during the late glorious police action in Korea, wherein I scored as a genuine hero. It was I who saved the company clipboard.

Blackstone, Virginia, enters, technicolor chancres and pustules scattered over its otherwise pastoral panorama of saloons, diners, tattoo parlors, and Army-Navy stores.

JIM JAM

(*staring moodily into his drink*)

In Blackstone, Virginia, I thought about you.

(*A lonely streetlamp in the fog falls on him.*)

JAMES JOYCE

And still a light moves long the river, 'deed it do.

SUSAN B. ANTHONY

(*involved in indescribable pleasures with Miss Gashe*)

I blush! I enflame! And yet! D-d-d-d-don't s-stop!

(*Her eyes roll calmly about in her head.*)

MARQUIS DE SADE

That's entertainment!

(*He hones his dirk, visibly moved.*)

DR. ELEAZAR SOD

(*in the final stages of an experiment that will differentiate shit from Shinola*)

Hmm. This substance has the exact molecular structure of a decayed fedora. What can it mean?

HARRY THE CRAB

Sod is one of the few critics from whom I have learned.

(*He learns.*)

BILLY McCOY

(*tickling the ivories*)

Guess I'll tickle the ivories.

AUDIENCE

Tickle those ivories, kid!
He's O.K. for an Irish!
He looks like a fuckin' priest to me!
Sing "My Mamma's Cannoli Was Holy To Me"!

SAL RONGO

American cheese and cole slaw on a roll is my delight! That's Friday food!

SENATOR STREET

(*rising from his bed of pain*)

Another ignorant ginzola heard from.

(Mother Cabrini drops a large float in honor of Santa Rosalia upon him.)

EDDY BESHARY

The good Senator is clearly a member of the bovine group with nationalist tendencies toward the order of orthoptera.

(He discovers a large cardboard box in which there is a map of Brooklyn.)

A map with the seemingly endless streets of the County of Kings meticulously in details and scaled to boots! With such a paradigm of the cartographer's art I may supplement my already exhausting knowledge of this remarkable environ, about which, I may addend, there is nothing funny.

FAIR YOUNG MAIDEN

(with a heavenly sigh)

I like the cut of his jib and the glint in his eye, the arrow of his song and the beg of his question. In short, a man!

EDDY BESHARY

It is of the utmost misfortune that this maiden is not a Frenchwoman. She is pulchritudinous, but what can she know of cafés, haute cuisine, and apéritifs in the mellow sunlight of a Paris afternoon, hah? She is a bumpkin, alas.

ALL sing:

Him give the girl of the even
And of the boulevards
Although this fair young maiden
May break the heart in shards.
The heart in shards.

The lass is alas! a bumpkin
In cotton underwear
Her pickles pies and jellies

Will not his heart ensnare
    His heart ensnare.

For O! He is an Arabian knight
A debonair son of a gun!
And her idea of a wonderful sight
Is a burger on toasted bun
    On a mayonnaised toasted bub-bun!

HARRY THE CRAB

I have been reduced to selling my literary archive to Max's Kansas City.

(*He weeps blood and has a beatific vision.*)

ODILE GASHE

That was indeed a shared moment of emotional release, Susan . . . May I call you Susan?

SUSAN B. ANTHONY

(*her body racked with the effects of her one hundred and tenth orgasm*)

Call me—anything—but don't call me—late for supper.

(*She affects a girlish smile.*)

MARQUIS DE SADE

A taste of the cat would cure the whore's levity.

FOOTS FUNGO

(*offstage*)

Strike *two*?! Jesus Christ, it looked high and outside to me!

CHARLES DEXTER WARD

Fungo is clearly being punished by the umpires for his outspoken stand on the intentional walk in order to get to—an unfortunate phrase—.002 hitters like himself. It is arbitrary punitive action.

(*He is metamorphosed into the American Civil Liberties Union.*)

SAL RONGO

Have a cheese sangwich, Charlie? It's Friday yet again.

(*aside*)

It's always Friday when you're a wop.

BROTHER OF SAL RONGO

Baloney on rye with relish, please.

SAL RONGO

(*lashing him with a scapular*)

You'll eat cheese!

JAMES JOYCE

(*sighing*)

Who brought us into the yellow world?

JACK ARMSTRONG

(*surfacing*)

Take all you want—eat all you take!

(*With powerful strokes he makes for shore.*)

DR. ELEAZAR SOD

I must face the fact that I can't tell shit from Shinola.

(*His entire laboratory decays.*)

EDDY BESHARY

(*consuming two jiggers of Old Grand-Dad bourbon whiskey and one glass of Ballantine lager beer*)

Rest assured that it was not loafing on the corner with varied ragamuffins and hooligans of the streets that bore Dr. Sod to his present apogee of pedagogical and didactical success. Rather, the nightly burning of the midnight oil and the diligent application to countless learned tomes gave him a glimpse of the summit, the Everest, which he has now scaled up.

(*He plays parcheesi, parchesi, parchisi, and pachisi.*)

In short, for the scientific brain there surceases efforts in no wise, ever. Questing forever for delusive truth is his wont!

JAMES JOYCE

Sheew gweatness was his twadgedy.

VINNIE PACHISI

(*directing a car which a friend of his is driving*)

Go fuckin' back, Ant'ny!

Ant'ny backs up and strikes a lonely vehicle which is discovered to be the team bus of the Amarillo Centipedes, on its way to Texas.

"SHOTGUN" JAREMA

(*alighting from the bus*)

What do you goddam ginzos think yer doin'?

SENATOR STREET

(*crawling out from beneath the float*)

Tell them, son! Tell them! They don't even look like Americans despite their infectiously warm smiles.

(*Elizabeth Street hurts him.*)

BETSY JEAN DAISY SMITH

It was an eyetalian street that did it, honey!

(She is surrounded by four Italo-American toughs who force her to attend a Jewish wedding at the Society for Ethical Culture.)

MARQUIS DE SADE

(disguised from the waist down as the groom)

Bella, bella ragazza!

(He strikes himself with his gold-knobbed cane.)

Yet another effort, Frenchmen!

Certain Frenchmen deftly make an EFFORT.

EFFORT

I am yet another effort, doomed for a certain time to walk the night.

JAMES JOYCE

He caught his death of fusiliers.

SEAN ALEXANDER KURKJIAN

His bed is dead.

FOOTS FUNGO

(from the window of the bus)

I haven't been gettin' around on the fast ball, that's all. Soon as it gets warm . . .

AUDIENCE

Trow the goddam bum out!
What kinda name is Fungo?

(They begin wrapping a fig tree in burlap and linoleum.)

A goddam busher!
Fuckin' hot dog!

ALICE BLUEGOWN

Will nod one among you blay the aggordion? The beaudy of its sounts rivals those of the drumpet.

JAMES JOYCE

They just spirits a body away.

VINNIE PACHISI

I'll play it honey—if you'll play the old skin flute!

(*He laughs raucously and opens clams.*)

The scene swiftly changes to show a calm lagoon or inlet of the sea, rising from which, light flashing from their pearly, polished interiors in such wise as to rival the effects of the very moonshine itself, are ten clam shells in which are seen reclining the noble Masquers of our entertainment. They are costumed to represent rich businessmen, rock stars, political reformers, high-priced whores, evangelists, talk-show hosts, great contemporary authors, radical activists, boring financial advisors, and celebrities of the media; in short, the cream of civilization. A babel-like din issues forth from the shells, which is understood to be interesting conversation. As if at a given signal, they all begin weeping angrily for The Poor, as a photograph of a Poor is passed from hand to hand. Intensely brilliant lights of variegated colors pass over their faces, which prove to be racked with pain. Yet, as swiftly as they wept, they cease to weep, and take on sternly courageous attitudes, listening intently to the Premier Clam, a hermaphroditic figure gorgeously arrayed in a silver jump suit on the chest of which, in flashing gems, is described the flag of the Viet Cong. He begins to sing the intense "I'll Give You Anything But Money" and the shells and their succulent occupants sink beneath the calm surface of the waters.

MARQUIS DE SADE

(*beaming*)

Little nippers!

SUSAN B. ANTHONY

(*toying with Miss Gashe's crewcut*)

In a certain light you resemble Emily Dickinson, Odile.

ODILE GASHE

I always thought of myself as being more the Miz Kipling type.

(*She turns into Tommy Atkins.*)

SUSAN B. ANTHONY

On second thought you *do* look like our brave Tommy!

DR. NESBIT

Atkins was never equipped like that! I knew him well when I served as regimental dental officer in the Punjab. There the beastly sun destroyed his molars. Lived on pap for a year before being demobbed and shipped back to Blighty.

CHARLES DEXTER WARD

Thus the fate of all imperialists! *Sic transit gloria limey.*

AUDIENCE

This guy sounds like a fuckin' kike jig to me!
Where's Patsy an' Carmine?
Send the basted an eel!
I know what he is—he's a fag, that's what he is!
A goddam Protestant fag!

OFFICER KILLARNEY

(*crossing himself*)

God bless the mark!

(*He subdues Mr. WARD for his own good.*)

SENATOR STREET

(*emerging painfully from the rubble of Elizabeth Street*)

Only an animal could stand that garlic.

(*A red pushcart runs him down.*)

DUCHESS

(*to TINKER*)

I've runs in my stockings, sir. Oh! You must think me ugly.

(*She attempts to cross her legs but is prevented from accomplishing this feat by the extraordinary position of the Tinker's body.*)

Don't—look—at—me!

(*Her eyes seek refuge in the heartless clouds.*)

TINKER

Unnhh, unnnhh, hunnnhh, ooofff . . .

JIM JAM

(*absently crushing his glass*)

The sound of whisp'ring lovers under a summer silv'ry moon makes me think about "her." I've got to forget.

A jukebox suddenly begins to play "Our Song Will Forever Linger So I'll Never Dare Forget."

CLARK SITZ

A brisk run around the block can supplement the therapeutic effects of a cold bath, as any Tenderfoot can tell you.

(*He ties a perfect sheepshank in his washcloth.*)

"SHOTGUN" JAREMA

(*boarding the bus*)

We been hittin' em, but right *at* people!

GENERAL KIDWELL

It was the thought of the peanuts and Cracker Jack at the old ballgame that stood us in good stead while we fled in wild disorder in old Frozen Chosen.

(*He worships a statue of Jesus Christ that glows in the dark.*)

LANCE DELRIO

An honest job at last, selling the yokels these famous statues that actually glow in the dark. The Mex makes good with Jesus.

VINNIE PACHISI

If that greaser took the name of the Lord thy God in vain I'll break his fuckin' teeth for him!

EDDY BESHARY

Can this be the same youth which at one time daily practiced "Lady of Spain" on the accordion? It impossible appears, yet—alas!—it is so. He has become nothing more than a pitiful crustacean on the floor of the ocean of life.

(*He reads* The Green Sheet *and selects a good loser.*)

VINNIE PACHISI

Watch your fuckin' mout', you joo basted!

HARRY THE CRAB

Perhaps you'd like to strike *me*, Mr. Pachisi? I am Harry, the Wandering Jew, just a sweaty kike off the streets, born to suffer, grovel, and die each dawn.

FUCKING WHORE

(*refastening her garters*)

I'm just a girl that men forget.

FOOTS FUNGO

When I *try* to hit home runs, my average drops.

There is general and prolonged hysterical laughter.

CHARLES DEXTER WARD

(*flushed with anger*)

These fans do not represent the People!

CLARK SITZ

(*mortifying the very flesh of himself with his knotted washcloth as he gazes on Miss Whore's splendid thighs*)

It's just my luck to be in love in vain.

TINKER

(*rolling off the entranced DUCHESS*)

Who's bloody next?

DUCHESS

It was my Playtex Cross-Your-Heart bra that caught the lecherous rogue's eye. There's something about a filthy, unwashed laboring man that attracts repressed noblewomen like me, as Lorenzo has noted oft.

(*She begins to levitate, her nether garments in tatters.*)

Blessèd be the unenlightened.

VINNIE PACHISI

(*striking HARRY THE CRAB*)

I gotta hand it to you mockie basteds! You really take advantage of an education.

EDDY BESHARY

This equine cockaroach wishes to bask in the reflected glow of true scholarship as exemplificated by the Job-like figure cut by Mr. Crab. It is unworthy of a Son of Italy.

AUDIENCE

What's that son of a bitch talkin' the Sons of Italy?
What is he, crazy?
He looks like a melanzan' to me!
He don't have no goddam respect!

(*They disappear into semi-detached brick houses.*)

JIM JAM

(*gazing down a deserted, misty street*)

Crab is real people.

CHARLES DEXTER WARD

These people have every Constitutional right to do as they please within the sacred confines of their own homes. Who dares deny them their Al Martino records? I will fight with every fiber of my being for the inalienable rights of these ignorant, fascist dagos!

CLARK SITZ

They make excellent plumbers, as any impartial survey will show.

(*He is suddenly trapped in a stall shower.*)

"SHOTGUN" JAREMA

If Fungo works out like we expect . . . no reason why . . . down to the wire.

MONSIGNOR O'HARA

God forgive him his little white lie. We all have our faults.

(*He slips into a black evening gown.*)

JAMES JOYCE

A vagrant need is a flagrant weed.

HURLEY LEES

That dress would fit Finn MacCool.

(He rattles his chains and four boys from Our Lady of Perpetual Help elementary school tell lies in the confessional.)

FATHER MAVOURNEEN

It's good to dig on these dudes getting out of that uptight religious bag. The church must change—or die!

(He grows a beard and reads Gary Snyder.)

ALL sing:

The Church must change—or die!
Give me that stern yet gentle sidewalk priest
    With beard and madras coat,
Roaming the ghetto streets like Je-Jesus Christ
    Himself.
He sees no mote in his brother's eye!
He loves the towns and the cities by God,
With some female companionship on the side
    Who's to censure him?
    Who? Not I!

The Church must not be U.S. Steel!
Where are those terrific guys, their shoes streaked
    With garbage and dust?
Although meditation is a pleasure, what
    Of the living God, by Christ?
Is the young Father's life not his own?
What if his close friend's name is Joan?
    Should his nerves forever quake?
    Give him a break!

Get the R.C. Church into the swim!
Let's see these cheery Padres with lovely lovers
    And winsome wives.
After a roll in the hay, by Christ, Divine Office
    Is not such a boring chore.
Should only the Protestants get their h--p?
The celebrant's only flesh and blood.
    A lissome lady in narrow bed
    Will aerate his head.

FOOTS FUNGO

I can't get those ribbies if there ain't nobody on base in front of me.

(*He shags flies.*)

SUSAN B. ANTHONY

(*mounting MISS GASHE*)

Will somebody tell Mr. Fungo that his worth as a man does not depend on how many "ribbies" he has?

(*She begins the dark act* con brio.)

What on earth is a ribby?

"SHOTGUN" JAREMA

He'll work out fine as a late-inning defensive replacement, sister! And do me a favor and mind your damn business, all right? Goddam broads don't know shit from Shinola about baseball . . .

DR. ELEAZAR SOD

Neither do our finest minds, simple friend.

DUCHESS

(*crawling across the diamond*)

Perhaps Mr. Fungo would prefer to shag me?

(*She rolls over wantonly.*)

Or would he rather I shagged *his* fly?

TINKER

It's noothin' but bloody fookin' rounders.

(*He bends about a venereal gaze.*)

LANCE DELRIO

(*bitterly*)

These rich Anglo broads never even consider that I'm flesh and blood too, right down to my worn huaraches from Sears. Can I help it if D. H. Lawrence thought I was a goddam snake or sumpn? Whcre now the brilliant *luces* of nighttime San Antone? Where the unbridled joy of Lawton, Oke? When do *I* get to drink the cocktails?

(*He affects the behavior of a shifty pimp.*)

Eef you spec' me to be peemp I be eet, señor. All sociologists know this is so, verdad?

(*He sells a tourist a naughty postcard starring a nun and a Spitz.*)

JAMES JOYCE

He ought to blush for himself.

FUCKING WHORE

It was a naughty postcard that started *me* on the road to shame. That, and an indecent proposal made me by an elderly gent, with car, whom I happened to encounter in the orchestra of the Carroll movie theater in sleepy, dreamy Brooklyn. When I placed my hand inside the popcorn container he held in his lap—

JAMES JOYCE

His lowness creeped out first via foodstuffs.

CHARLES DEXTER WARD

The replacement, within a popcorn container, of its legitimate contents by a more or less erect male organ, all cloaked in the darkness of a movie theater, may be construed as being an attempt to deceive the innocent young woman who has been led to believe that her searching hand will encounter popcorn, *just* popcorn, and nothing *but* popcorn, so help me God.

FUCKING WHORE

My hand and rights were grossly violated! If my hand happened to move in a gently stroking vertical motion when it encountered the contents of the container—blame it on my youth and my aborted artistic efforts.

(*She sobs as a huge poster of Pete Fountain is held up.*)

My lost king!

(*Shrieks.*)

VINNIE PACHISI

(*with a bulge in both slacks and throat*)

Even when ya humped her she used t' sing an' all. She was sorta like—like yuh kid sister.

(*He becomes Pat O'Brien.*)

JAMES JOYCE

Commit no miracles.

(*He prays aloud from* The Blue Book of Eccles.)

HARRY THE CRAB

My boils are drying up!

(*He throws away his ichthammol ointment to a crescendo of sorts.*)

I'll fight for the kid! Who knows better than me what heartaches are?

KID SISTER

You wouldn't doom a mate like me to a plight like that with a yid like this?

GENERAL KIDWELL

Yids can't fight. They hang around the day room and go on sick call.

HARRY THE CRAB

That's *plight*, you warmonger.

JACK ARMSTRONG

Who recalls the whispered term of opprobrium for the United States Coast Guard? Let's hear it, gang!

AUDIENCE

THE JEWISH NAVY!

(*They walk off, carrying stone lions, iron flamingoes and Negro jockeys, and divers rolls of gaily flowered linoleum; they then descend into basements and play Hearts.*)

SENATOR STREET

Unbelievably poor taste. Ignorant meatballs!

(*He has a heart attack on Mulberry Street and is roundly ignored.*)

A nice place to visit but . . .

(*He dies and becomes Calvin Coolidge.*)

JAMES JOYCE

The good go and the wicked is left over.

BETSY JEAN DAISY SMITH

(*weeping prettily into her Bonwit scarf*)

Oh sugar, sugar! Only I understood you, only I knew the unbelievable pressures of your office.

UNBELIEVABLE PRESSURES

It is true. Only this devoted sec'y knew us.

CHAIR

How will I be able to forget the pressure of her girlish thighs and warm heinie?

(*The CHAIR is carried off to the Salvation Army warehouse where it is sold to a mocking Socialist.*)

AIRMAN SMITH

I'll take her back. I'll forgive her every error, far-flung though I may be. Don't I have the Good Conduct medal for eating up all my chow?

USO

Remember him, America. Remember him. If you don't, who will?

(*The USO gazes off toward the sea.*)

JAMES JOYCE

Respect the uniform.

(*He disappears into the archive at Dalkey.*)

HARRY THE CRAB

Senator Street knew the aspirations of the little man. Who can forget or long deny the hours he spent as Chairman of the American United National and Transworld Boil and Carbuncle Foundation? The telethons on which he pretended to be Jerry Lewis or some other thing? How he gravely stood in pelting rain to promise youth things?

FUCKING WHORE

(*bravely*)

It was through his efforts that the Old Joe was virtually stamped out in the immaculate barracks of Camp Pickett.

JAMES JOYCE

Stamp out bad eggs.

OLD JOE

(*rattling a tambourine*)

Just because my teeth are pearly, my head is bending low.

FOOTS FUNGO

(*playing pepper and ignoring the DUCHESS*)

He could figure slugging averages!

(*He is breathless with awe and a slow-hit grounder goes between his legs.*)

VINNIE PACHISI

But the basted wouldn't except the axpirations of the Italo-American community.

AUDIENCE

(*worshiping a bas-relief frieze depicting Mario Lanza, Julius LaRosa, Al Martino, Dean Martin, Lou Monte, Jimmy Roselli, Steve Rossi, Jerry Vale, Frank Sinatra, Enzo Stuarti, Tony Bennett, and Sergio Franchi as the twelve disciples, strong teeth flashing, caught for posterity's delight in an eternally joyous tarantella*)

How come he never talked up guys like Enrico Fermi?
Jimmy Durante?
Cesare Cazzabianco?
Yeah! Yeah!
Always somebody like Vincent Coll! How come?

That basted was a fuckin' harp anyway!

(*They leave for a reception on New Utrecht Avenue.*)

OFFICER KILLARNEY

(*awakening from a refreshing nap in his patrol car parked beneath the Brooklyn Bridge*)

Watch yer dirthy ignorant mouths or I'll make a collar!

(*The Emerald Society elects him Chief Gem.*)

SEAN ALEXANDER KURKJIAN

His bean is green.

DR. ELEAZAR SOD

(*emerging, dazed, from his razed laboratory*)

Sod's occupation's gone!

(*He is given a large grant to study The Decay of Laboratories.*)

EDDY BESHARY

Lucidly, it is clear that years of dedication and discipline have enabled the good doctor to plunge into fecal matter and emerge emitting the effluvia of a rose, if one may so to speak. In some ways he brings to mind the beetle, *Gymnopleurus pilularius*, although hastening, I attest that I speak not out of pejorativeness or obloquy, that is, I am not labeling the learned doc a repulsive coleoptera.

(*He cuts down corner lampposts with fervid zeal.*)

JAMES JOYCE

Thud.

FAIR YOUNG MAIDEN

(*revealing, for the first time in her life, her knees*)

I'm sorely tempted to give up my precious jewel to this flower of the U.A.R.

EDDY BESHARY

[illegible]

(*He manfully undoes his trousers.*)

FAIR YOUNG MAIDEN

(*a picture of health*)

I hope I can please you, sir.

(*She puts out her tongue.*)

FOOTS FUNGO

(*sliding into second but failing to break up the double play*)

I missed the hit-and-run sign.

HURLEY LEES

(*staring at the point where the trembling flesh of the FAIR YOUNG MAIDEN meets that of EDDY BESHARY*)

Nothing like this ever happened in the ould sod atall, atall.

DR. ELEAZAR SOD

(*drawing himself up haughtily*)

I am not old, sir, but, rather, mature.

FATHER MAVOURNEEN

Some unreconstructed Catholics still think such an act an instance of bestiality, rather than the thing of beauty it can be between two loving and mutually consenting adults.

(*He chants the* Kyrie, *accompanying himself on a genuine San Francisco autoharp.*)

BILLY McCOY

(*improvising harmony to the priest's lively tune*)

That's a catchy little melody, Padre, but I don't feature those lyrics.

(*He is afflicted with boils on his fingers.*)

HARRY THE CRAB

A word with Miss Whore may cure your disgusting malady. Take a chance!

FUCKING WHORE

Just touch my heart of gold.

(*aside*)

I was always a sucker for piano players.

BILLY McCOY

(*collapsing before he can reach her*)

I know now that life is a mysterious nothing.

(*He dies a good Catholic death and goes to hell as THE SPIRIT OF CARMEN CAVALLARO.*)

JAMES JOYCE

He is quieter now.

THE SPIRIT OF CARMEN CAVALLARO

(*at the gate of hell*)

I chure like to ainter eento deez plaze. Look like a lodda fone!

VOICE OF SATAN

Deliveries in the rear, spick!

FOOTS FUNGO

(*anally violating the DUCHESS as the old shadows gather in old center field*)

You're my can o' corn, baby!

DUCHESS

And you're my bad hop. Whoooooo!

TINKER

(*still searching for fresh prey*)

I'll fook the bloody umpires in a bloody minute!

MONSIGNOR O'HARA

(*straightening the seams of his black mesh stockings*)

Oh, Tinker! Oh, Mr. Tinker! May I have a word with you?

SEAN ALEXANDER KURKJIAN

His ass is glass. His anus is heinous.

AIRMAN SMITH

(*arriving at the ballpark*)

I've been invited to kiss and fondle Old Glory during the big pre-game ceremonies . . . am I late?

JAMES JOYCE

What a picture primitive!

(*He chuckles as if seeing him for the first time.*)

"SHOTGUN" JAREMA

The game's in the bottom of the ninth, kid. But God bless you!

You're a credit to those Thousands of American Boys glued to tiny radios in those far-flung outposts all over the world.

AIRMAN SMITH

I wanted to offer my kiss and fondle for the repose of the soul of Senator Street, my wife's late friend and compassionate employer.

FATHER MAVOURNEEN

I hate that goddam kinda talk.

(*God turns him into a Presbyterian.*)

THE SPIRIT OF CARMEN CAVALLARO

(*ripping into a medley of best-loved songs of the American people*)

I 'ave bin coll "the Poet of the Piano."

(*Frederic Chopin strikes him with a grand piano.*)

SUSAN B. ANTHONY

It's clear that they share a strong, enlightened interest in music.

JAMES JOYCE

I'm blest if I can see.

FUCKING WHORE

The same sort of short-lived interest Mr. McCoy and I once shared—how long ago it all seems.

(*She breaks down and is carried off to a modern-dance class.*)

Here the scene wherein she stands, being the warmly cluttered studio of a second-rate dance teacher, mediocre musician, and all-around sweet guy with a lot of terrifically interesting opinions, changes, and in place of it appears a desolate expanse of open country cunningly constructed to resemble Fort Hood, Texas. Spread out in battalion formation across the field, at parade rest, their boyish hands furtively clutching ragged and well-read copies of Guinea Red, *are Thousands of American Boys, lost in secret thought. Their stern yet homely faces twitch as they manfully struggle to hold back the hot tears that are summoned to their eyes as, faintly, and in largo tempo, a chorus of McCoy's famous "Wurlitzer Woogie" is heard, moving gently, almost diffidently, through the aromatic dust of Central Texas. They think of home and high art as the scene slowly changes back to the strangely empty, yet—not empty—studio. McCoy's piece is heartbreakingly punctuated by the fading sobs of Miss WHORE.*

FUCKING WHORE

There's no point in trying to return to the past!

(*She has a vision of a Chinese laundryman holding tenderly a handkerchief in his hand.*)

THE SPIRIT OF CARMEN CAVALLARO

(*faintly, from beneath the ruins of the piano*)

Now *that's* what I coll the reepling of the reethum! Sunumabeetch!

EDDY BESHARY

In the empty penthouse erstwhile vacated by the suddenness and tragical demisement of "Ivories" McCoy, the Rolls-Royce impeccability of piano artistry, there shall be installed in genteel domesticity, if God is just, as oft he proves, the poet of the piano, Carmine Caballo, the connoisseur's Liszt!

THE SPIRIT OF CARMEN CAVALLARO

Thees ees *not* my llama, Arab maldito!

The sound of enraged Latin-American nationalists is heard off stage.

FOOTS FUNGO

Gladys Gooding was always *my* meat! When she tore into "Tioo Tioo" I got a chill just *all* up my spine!

(*He drifts lazily out under a towering pop-up and falls over second base.*)

ALICE BLUEGOWN

Is dat whad you call bazeball? Id's zo beaudiful id remints me of ard. Id is lige life idself. Fraughd wid trama!

"SHOTGUN" JAREMA

All the world's a ballpark, and in it we poor players are the Phillies.

(*He thinks, and as he does so is slowly transformed into Otto Kruger, after which he ascends to a cloud or two.*)

MARQUIS DE SADE

(*applauding*)

Way to go!

ODILE GASHE

For one of such prosaic vision, it is a magnificent secession.

CLARK SITZ

(*hopefully studying the clouds*)

Perhaps there will be a rain delay?

JIM JAM

The smell of the dugout . . . the warmth of the beer . . . the sweating, shouting crowds . . .

(*He wanders into a fog bank.*)

BETSY JEAN DAISY SMITH

It was the unbelievable pressures of the job that caused the wily pilot's metamorphosis, God love him.

UNBELIEVABLE PRESSURES

We *caused* nothing, young woman. We merely, ah, suggested . . . a change might be to the mutual benefit of the players and Mr. Jarema, as well as being indicative of the belief that our fans deserve a team that can place itself in contention. We can't get rid of the players, so . . .

FOOTS FUNGO

(*going deep into the hole and throwing wild past first base*)

He told me to shorten up on the old lumber. I'll never let the skipper down!

SEAN ALEXANDER KURKJIAN

His advice was nice.

CHARLES DEXTER WARD

It is the act of an elitist, nothing more or less. As the young people, who are of course the hope of the future as well as of liberated art might say, Jarema copped out. Right on! Heavy! Rip off! Dynamite!

DR. NESBIT

You can't tell a boy from a girl anymore, thank God.

(*He proceeds to fill a patient's ear.*)

This will only be temporary until this strange opening in your ear closes up.

FOOTS FUNGO

I'm not pullin' the ball to left as much as I did when I played in the bigs.

(*With the tying run in scoring position he fouls out to the catcher.*)

ALICE BLUEGOWN

Is thad a goot hid?

(*She sits on a discarded wiener.*)

Who's thad? Don'd I know you?

DISCARDED WIENER

I think you are confusing me.

JACK ARMSTRONG

(*emerging from the briny*)

Which way is Ebbets Field? I want to see those Beloved Buns! Not too surprising for a military man, eh? *And* a onetime altar boy!

(*He admires his shoulder boards and writes a letter to his folks.*)

OLD JOE

Just because my hair is curly, I hear those gentle voices calling.

(*He dances a happy jig.*)

SEAN ALEXANDER KURKJIAN

His feet are neat. The jig is trig.

JIM JAM

I remember the smell of the Old Man rolling, rolling along. His dread and muddy might.

(*He orders a nightcap in a small, deserted bar at the end of a pier.*)

You'd never know it, but buddy, I'm a kinda poet.

ROBERTO BLIGH

Poems are made by fools like me.

(*He makes a tree.*)

JAMES JOYCE

It gives furiously to think.

MARQUIS DE SADE

Sacré bleu! I'd like to fill the dabbler up with a goodly portion of that rascally *Treponema pallidum*.

DUCHESS

Is that you in the on-deck circle, Foots?

(*She is escorted none too gently off the field and arrested for indecent exposure.*)

Haven't any of you gentlemen ever seen a lady's foundation garments before? Don't you read *The New York Times*?

SUSAN B. ANTHONY

The cruel corset was invented by the barons of the whaling industry and other capitalist swine.

ODILE GASHE

Bone and lacing freaks!

JAMES JOYCE

I led the life.

BETSY JEAN DAISY SMITH

That cruel oppression has been lifted. My girlish lower torso is now concealed only by the most feminine of gossamer panties, the sheerest of weightless panty hose without seams to cut and bind, the lightest of scrumptious bodyshirts with delightfully convenient snap crotch, and the briefest of provocative shorts. Freedom at last! I guess you might say I'm that cosmopolitan girl.

JACK ARMSTRONG

Some of the fellows in the fleet call her something else!

VINNIE PACHISI

To plug the broad you gotta be Jimmy Valentine!

FUCKING WHORE

Just to make tinkle is an act of faith. God bless her courage!

CHARLES DEXTER WARD

Down with Captain Ahab! It is with such young women that the hope of the future lies!

HOPE OF THE FUTURE

Unfortunately, by the time she disrobed, it was too late to lie with her.

MARQUIS DE SADE

Give me the old-time religion.

OLD JOE

Because I like to dress a babe up in the latest style, I'm a comin'.

(He shoots crap and drinks gin.)

SMALL GROUP OF WEALTHY TEXANS

That is why they call him Shine!

EDDY BESHARY

Miss Smith possesses little of the *éclat* of the women of Paris or Cairo, nor is her belonging the mysterious muliebrity of the babes of glowing cities of the ilk of Copenhagen or Amsterdam—yet, her beauty to wit declares itself of inordinate puissance. Frankly speaking, had I a brief moment or two with her in crepuscular hallway or on the shadowy and comfy, or even not so comfy back seat of a Chevrolette or Ford, I would instantly haul her ashes.

(*He admires her from afar, hand in pocket.*)

ALL sing:

When as in scanties Betsy goes,
Then, Arab Eddy's member grows,
And, he manipulates his hose!

Next, do his dark eyes brilliantly
Down to her undies try to see;
O how he groaneth shamelessly.

FAIR YOUNG MAIDEN

Unrequited love's a bore.

THE SPIRIT OF CARMEN CAVALLARO

'Ow 'bout a liddle glass of coquito, baby? A short cerveza? You like maybe to esmoke a reefer?

(*The lights dim as the poet of the piano plays a selection of Mort Ancul favorites. Central Park hovers menacingly in the background for the briefest of moments.*)

FAIR YOUNG MAIDEN

I fear that drugs or liquor may completely undo me. They may well lead to a lowering of that moral guard that has long saved me from the sins of the flesh.

HARRY THE CRAB

That's *fletch*!

FATHER MAVOURNEEN

The lies of frustrated priests and repressed nuns. Live, girl, live! Move to the polyglot streets of the Lower East Side and mix with the restless lives of the steamy People! Take to the rooftops and cellars! Drunk on cheap wine and bloated with greasy food let your sweet youthful passions hold sway at last.

(*He takes her hand.*)

Care to crash in my groovy pad, baby? It's very heavy. Day-glo walls and wondrously boring old rock posters from San Francisco? Coupla big sterling silver dynamite crucifixes to hang around your neck?

MONSIGNOR O'HARA

(*disguised as a wanton high school girl*)

Got room for three, handsome?

GOD

That does it for those two. I'm afraid that this has become just a bit too much of an embarrassment for all concerned.

(*He sentences them both to Purgatory for 30 million years.*)

JAMES JOYCE

Now have thy children entered into their habitations.

FOOTS FUNGO

I don't see that much difference in playin' third.

(*A line drive tears his glove off and the winning run comes home. He is removed from the game and sold outright for $45 to the Biloxi Crips.*)

I'm sure I'll be able to help the team. They're a great buncha guys.

JAMES JOYCE

One must sell it to someone, the sacred name of love.

"CRACKER" YALOBUSHA

(*eating a chili dog*)

Ah know this ol' boy kin he'p the team. Ah plan to bring him in in the late quarters when we ten, twelve points behin'.

(*Someone hands him a baseball and he looks at it with unconcealed suspicion.*)

What y'all handin' me heah, boy? Some kinda kiddie toy?

ROBERTO BLIGH

He has a nest of robins in his hair.

LANCE DELRIO

(*going back to his roots on the West side of San Antonio*)

The maricón has even expropriated our native food.

(*He joins a ragged band of Villistas and shoots his big toe off in an excess of Latin joy.*)

JIM JAM

I want to get a few bucks together and get my things out of the cleaners before I hit that lonesome old road to nowhere.

ROBERTO BLIGH

His hungry mouth was pressed.

THE SPIRIT OF CARMEN CAVALLARO

Thees Joyz Keelmer was some terreefic broad, hah?

EDDY BESHARY

Oft have I bended my sloe-eyed glance of Araby upon her verses. Culture is more than a GGG suit with extra pants for those casual weekends with the sporty coats.

"CRACKER" YALOBUSHA

This ol' boy talks like one o' them New Yoke spo'ts writers.

(*He looks at a Louisville Slugger incredulously.*)

FOOTS FUNGO

(*on the bench*)

Y' gotta be in the right frame of mind to come off the bench cold as a pinch hitter and watch that third strike go by.

JAMES JOYCE

You are pure. You are pure.

"CRACKER" YALOBUSHA

A goo-ood ol' *boy*!

(*gesturing toward the bat he has been examining*)

What in the *hell* is this god-daym stick?

DUCHESS

Like every rotten man who has ever walked the earth, the little dear has gone out of my life.

JIM JAM

Inconstant and fleeting as the scent of magnolia over the dark'ning countryside.

(*He boards a lonesome train in pelting rain. To the DUCHESS*)

I'll peek through the crack and look at the track.

SUSAN B. ANTHONY

Take off your skirts and lie down, darling. In a certain light you bear an uncanny resemblance to Sappho, a dynamite babe!

DUCHESS

That man, inconstant though he may be, is peer of the gods.

(*She lies down, suddenly deshabille.*)

Is it his fault that he can't hit the high hard one? Or the sneaky fast one? Or the big curve? Or the dinky slider? And nobody can hit the unpredictable knuckler!

(*She is made an honorary Philly fan.*)

Others have overcome shortcomings as grievous. One thinks of Choo-Choo Coleman, Elio Chacón, Charley Neal.

HURLEY LEES

Bullshit and broken glass!

(*He frightens the City of Philadelphia by there appearing in a Pirate uniform.*)

SUSAN B. ANTHONY

(*brandishing her foxed copy of* A Right-On Guide To Lesbian Joy)

Who is this loutish Celt? The Board of Health should have him arrested for carrying his ass too near the ground.

(*She smiles, as if remembering something.*)

MARQUIS DE SADE

Ass? Where? Who?

(*He enters a comfort station precipitately.*)

LANCE DELRIO

(*limping and bemedaled*)

An old war wound I got fighting for my People's right to be astronauts. I don't want to talk about it just now.

(*Tears form in his depthless eyes as an orchestra strikes up the lively "La Luna Caramba Azúl, Corazón!"*)

ALICE BLUEGOWN

Dhere's someding aboud a soltier . . .

(*She turns into Lupe Velez.*)

FUCKING WHORE

Actually, it was I who was responsible for Señor DelRio's wound —I drove him to a sense of his duty to the People by giving him a subtle taste of the Old Joe. Not even the debonair are immune to persuasion.

OLD JOE

Just because I always wear a smile, I always wear a smile.

(*He shuffles into Queens and the entire population flees to Suffolk County.*)

ROBERTO BLIGH

In his joyous primal innocence, he looks at God all day.

VINNIE PACHISI

Watch your faggot mout' about God!

DR. ELEAZAR SOD

My early findings seem to point to a similarity in the process of decay in fedoras and laboratories alike. Although it is too soon to be absolutely sure, they both appear to possess the identical molecular structure of Shinola.

(*His stern head is bathed in an unearthly golden light.*)

JAMES JOYCE

Note his sleek hair, so elegant, *tableau vivant.*

JIM JAM

(*alighting from the 12:02 in a lonesome old town*)

Time to sling the old raincoat over the shoulder, or shoulders.

(*He slings.*)

I'm just a stranger in town.

(*His raincoat falls into a sad puddle.*)

My old raincoat has slipped from my shoulders and fallen into a sad, a sad and grey puddle.

Once again, by means of the judiciously expert and perfectly executed movement of scena ductilis, *we are returned to the ballpark seen at the beginning of our entertainment. The Masquers have been transformed from players of the game into a softly humming group of clean-cut youths, which worshiping body forms a perfect circle around second base, toward which "sack" their eyes are fervently bent. At first glance, it would seem that they are rapt in adoration of the inanimate object but a closer look reveals the* MINUSCULE FIGURE OF TY COBB, *dressed in his at-home whites, sandwich boards hanging nonchalantly from his shoulders. On both front and rear of these boards is displayed the mystical number, 367. As the tiny figure prepares to speak, his mouth slowly opening, the Masquers softly sing a medley of the following songs of the diamond:* He Strides to the Mound With the Latest Disease; I Want to Get Some Wood On It So Bad; The Sneaky Slider Made a Rattler Rider Outta Me; The Ballad of the 15.00 ERA; I've Got Splinters In My Ring-Dang-Doo; I've Come To Love My Pine-Tar Rag; They Weren't Falling In For Us (That Sunny Day); I Lost It In the Glare; He Hit .200 ('Cause They Played Him Every Day); His Smoke Got In Their Eyes; In Deep Center, There You Feel Free; *and* Let His Bunt Roll Foul! *Then the tiny player speaks, with a voice of thunder.*

MINUSCULE FIGURE OF TY COBB

Fungo, you have been taking your eye off the ball halfway through your swing. I have noticed this in Baseball Heaven, and so I have returned to earth to caution you about it; let's say a little bird told me. Keep your eye everlastingly on the ball, Fungo, and the game will be good to you as it was good to me, despite the incursions of the latinos and nigras who have almost ruined it. Spikes high! Stick it in his ear! Put it in his teeth! No quarter! Hit 'em where they ain't! Run it out! Wait for your pitch! Break up the double play! No defense against the homer!

(*He begins to fade away as fog and drizzle close in on the ballpark.*)

Farewell, Fungo, farewell, it is time to take the eternal field . . . farewell . . . eye on the old pill . . .

(*He disappears. The Masquers buy programs.*)

FOOTS FUNGO

(*staring about, bewildered, as if awakening from a heroic dream*)

I heard the voice of . . . the old Georgia Peach . . . he told me . . . to keep my eye on the ball! It is the secret! How simple it all seems now. Everything true and beautiful must converge.

JAMES JOYCE

A dream of favours, a favourable dream.

AUDIENCE

Maybe now we'll see some *ball*!
I don't believe the phony basted!
They don't make ballplayers like they useta!
Why don't the bitch at the organ play some Italian songs?

(*Sniffling, they gaze at photos of Joe DiMaggio. Mothers and aunts in black carry in Bath Beach and hoist it to the ceiling where it becomes a giant tomato plant.*)

DUCHESS

(*swiftly rising from her supine position and as swiftly adjusting her garments and tidying her appearance*)

What—what am I doing here? Have I grossly misjudged the moral code of the young athlete?

JAMES JOYCE

Simply killing, how she tidies her hair.

FOOTS FUNGO

I'm gonna lay back for the fast ball and—

(*He swings and crashes a homer into the fifteenth row of the upper mezzanine, 410 feet away. The ball strikes a bearded homosexual and the crowd goes wild.*)

"CRACKER" YALOBUSHA

Ah doan know whut they all cheerin' for, but they must be somethin' good about losin' the goddaym ball.

(*He begins whittling at the bat in his hands.*)

SUSAN B. ANTHONY

Have I gone mad that I should stand, flushed and uncorseted, before these all-American lads, fans all?

(*She retires to the ladies' room, foundation garments in hand.*)

AUDIENCE

Hit another faggot creep, Foots!
Woffuckin' power!
Since when do queers get allowed in the ballpark?
Hit one for the Dook!

JAMES JOYCE

(*to FOOTS*)

Will you carry my can and fight the fairies?

"CRACKER" YALOBUSHA

That's what ah call a *touchdown*, Foots. You play ball better than a damn nigra.

LANCE DELRIO

One of the finest examples of sportsmanship and sheer grit it has ever been my pleasure to witness.

(His war wound heals and he becomes an iconoclastic yet intelligent sportscaster.)

SMALL GROUP OF WEALTHY TEXANS

See how y'all can be deceived? We thought that ol' boy was a Mex. Instead, he turns out to be a smart Jewboy.

ROBERTO BLIGH

Foots bends his beefy arms today.

JIM JAM

In every single window I see her face.

(He sets fire to a Lucky and disappears into the rich, flavorful smoke.)

BETSY JEAN DAISY SMITH

That sweet budding superstar has shown me, by his example, that it is wicked of me to desire the freedom of my body.

(She begins to peel off her layers of free, modern clothing but her good intentions are stymied by a recalcitrant snap crotch.)

VINNIE PACHISI

I'll help ya, honey.

(The gods of the Swamp League cripple his clutching fingers. At the same moment, the snap crotch of her fun bodyshirt disintegrates.)

BETSY JEAN DAISY SMITH

It is a sign! A sign!

(She weeps.)

DR. ELEAZAR SOD

(shaking with excitement)

This unexpected decay factor sheds new light on my "fedora theory." Can it be that snap crotches were in use in late nineteenth-century Latvia? It might explain the preponderance of impotence in that ill-fated land beyond the sea. I wonder . . . ?

(*He goes on wondering, assuming the visage of Walter Pidgeon.*)

FOOTS FUNGO

(*lining a double off the left-field wall*)

He meant to get a curve down and in but he hung it on me. My eyes, of course, followed it all the way, and . . .

HARRY THE CRAB

The feeling has returned to my ankles! My blackheads are saying bye-bye! I feel new power and confidence as my body odor diminishes markedly!

(*He gambols with five rabid Dobermans.*)

ODILE GASHE

For the first time in my life, I'd like to perform the act of shame with a man.

(*She is obscured by a puff of smoke and emerges from it dressed as Pola Negri.*)

By heavens, I don't look half-bad.

JAMES JOYCE

I rose up one maypole morning and saw in my glass how nobody loves me but you.

"SHOTGUN" JAREMA

(*from the clouds*)

I always knew that the boy had all the tools. He could do it all, I knew. Thank God he has listened to that ultimate voice, I mean the one that is inside every man and a woman or two.

THE SPIRIT OF CARMEN CAVALLARO

For thees player of beisbol, I dedicate some of the All-Time Mageek Museec of Hollywood.

(*He dozes off as his rippling fingers perform.*)

SUSAN B. ANTHONY

(*reappearing from out of the ladies' room*)

There! Suitably bound once more by those cruel unmentionables that make us true women, I stand modestly among those who honor Mr. Fungo and his incredible triumph over adversity and plain old rotten ballplaying. A woman's place is in her stays.

SEAN ALEXANDER KURKJIAN

Her waist is chaste.

JIM JAM

(*in an alley from which the sunshine has drifted*)

Is her figure less than sleek? Is her chest a trifle meek? Stays, Susan Anthony, stays!

HARRY THE CRAB

My ankles! They are actually supporting my entire weight as I gambol with the Katzenjammer Kids here!

(*He eats a crushed pigeon.*)

DUCHESS

(*striking the TINKER as he attempts to force her into an unnatural act*)

How dare you even think of such venery, you pig, in the presence of a long-ball hitter and never-say-die hustler?

TINKER

The fookin' rounders player's turned her into a bloody nun.

(*Grumbling, he returns to Australia.*)

OLD JOE

(*striding toward the Queens-Brooklyn border, straight and proud in his new-found manhood*)

If dat fuckin' honky, Fungo, can git it on, so can I!

(*He turns into a People and puts the torch to De Camptown Racetrack.*)

FUCKING WHORE

The Old Joe has gone militant. Woe to the innocent pudenda of unwary lovers . . . science has shown that even nice people get the whoopsie. I stand before you all as a girl who might have married even Fungo had I stuck to the old clarinet, the old dance, the old magic of art.

(*She breaks down as a stranger across a crowded room plays "Limelight."*)

FOOTS FUNGO

(*starting a triple play with the stab of a screaming liner to third*)

I got no time for women. Occasional self-abuse to keep the eye clear and the hand steady—that's my speed. May God forgive me.

GOD

I forgive all .320 hitters and flashy infielders.

SEAN ALEXANDER KURKJIAN

All love his glove.

EDDY BESHARY

While I too am ensnared in the infectuous spirit of Fungo's feats and his admirable reversal of execrational forms as an athlete of the diamond, may I point my digit at the fact that though the teeny-tiny figure of Mr. Cobb, the plum of Georgia, had a salubrious effect on the beloved Fungo, all may not be attributed to miraculous fortune when it comes to his startling amelioration? In other words, it was sedulous application to the divers skills one needs to master that was of no small minute in his sudden ascent to stardom's precincts. I have seen often the same thing occur in the streets of Istanbul with rotten players of their national pastime, the name of which contest slips away from my cerebrum. Once again, it is the tale of the express elevator to the roof.

(*He whistles "Lola," happy as a Bedouin.*)

JAMES JOYCE

I believe in Dublin and the Sultan of Turkey.

FOOTS FUNGO

(*trotting out to his position*)

Don't throw bouquets at me. Just let me pose in my glove.

JACK ARMSTRONG

I suddenly feel as if I've grown something approaching a real ass!

(*His well-cut trousers are burst asunder by his burgeoning nates.*)

"POP" HEART

So faith and beauty again triumph over fleeting fame! Go, young Jack, to drab obscurity . . . it's better that way.

(*Printer's ink courses proudly through his old veins.*)

JAMES JOYCE

(*aside*)

He was grey at three.

MARQUIS DE SADE

The young officer's callipygian charms pale next to Fungo's flawless play. I fear that I may be forever cured.

(*He slaps his leg and emits what may well turn out to be his last joyous howl of pain.*)

ROBERTO BLIGH

Lonely Sade can break a knee.

SAL RONGO

I'm still fuckin' stoopid, but happy as a bitch that the Crips got a chance to win it all this year.

BROTHER OF SAL RONGO

Sal's a real stoopid, but a million warm laughs.

(*He sneaks some forbidden liverwurst into the source of his own warm laugh.*)

JIM JAM

(*over a lonely meal in an empty waterfront café*)

They call him frivolous Sal.

WUN EM EN

We'd be very interested in a book on the rebirth, as it were, of Fungo, done by a romantic loser and top writer who frequents waterfront cafés and can hardly believe that last year he was nobody. Fog walkers preferred. It'd be nice to sit down over a beer with someone like that and talk advances—someone real and warm, someone who's been around, someone with a fresh point of view, someone with a lousy agent.

(*He shuffles through his credit cards and appears briefly at several college symposia on the modern novel.*)

CLARK SITZ

How about a humorous treatment on the history of soap and water? I can tell it to somebody! Pick me up quick, top acquisitions man, for I may never wash again! This diamond dust on my epidermis feels like silk. I have seen the sign!

"SHOTGUN" JAREMA

(*booming from a cloud over left field*)

He's pickin' up the signs?

ROBERTO BLIGH

He wonders lonely in a cloud.

HARRY THE CRAB

Isn't that *crowd*?

FAIR YOUNG MAIDEN

(*aside*)

Sans boils, carbuncles, and other pustules, I am strangely attracted to this hairy Hebe.

SEAN ALEXANDER KURKJIAN

Her cunny feels funny.

AIRMAN SMITH

(*from the same cloud*)

Glad to have you aboard, sir!

"SHOTGUN" JAREMA

Hi there, yardbird! Ain't you the young feller who wanted to kiss and fondle Old Glory? Friend o' baseball's a friend o' mine!

RITA RIGHT

(*alighting from the crack Omaha Speedball*)

Even 'way out on the forever brooding plains, we know of Foots Fungo's feats through the magic of television.

(*Sings:*)

O Fungo Foots, your doubles and your triples
Make hearts to race, and stiffen girlish nipples,
And when o'er far-flung fence you crack the ball
Each lady in the stands doth come withal.

(*She suits actions to words and a festive crowd gathers around her joy-racked flesh.*)

HURLEY LEES

Everyone's so happy, begob, I can't even scare a bleeding Lutheran.

(*He returns to the ould sod, chains muffled.*)

ALICE BLUEGOWN

(*as Lupe Velez*)

I tango weeth any damn body I feel so sonomagum good!

(*To EDDY BESHARY*)

'Ey, beeg boy—'ow 'bout jou? Jou like to dance weeth Loop, hah?

(*She reveals her lower torso which is strangely suffused with a maidenly crimson.*)

JAMES JOYCE

I rise, O fair assemblage!

EDDY BESHARY

Although somewhat of the rube still clings to you, madam, and although there is little with which you may self-commend to a cosmopolite like myself, your lower limbs and so forth fill me with erotic bents. Let us retire to the darkened balcony of the

Electra moving-picture theater, where our bodies may perspire and blend.

ALICE BLUEGOWN

Your leeps spik bad Eengleesh, but there's jes, jes in jour pants!

KID SISTER

You wouldn't send a spick like her up in the dark like that with a dud like this?

BETSY JEAN DAISY SMITH

(*resplendently svelte in her new long-leg four-way power-net double-diamond panty girdle with nylon-lace appliqué magic-oval tummy flattener and concealed detachable garters*)

Let the child know the joys of sex before she takes the irreversible step toward responsible womanhood.

(*Since she cannot sit down, she stands up straight and tall.*)

DR. NESBIT

I had a passing filthy thought, but let it go.

(*He closes his office and goes to the ballgame.*)

CHARLES DEXTER WARD'

This is the true American way, when young people of varying minority groups can submerge their differences in the satisfaction of their raging lusts. I believe Engels had a paragraph or two about it . . . no matter.

JAMES JOYCE

Here let a few artifacts fend in their own favour.

OFFICER KILLARNEY

I'll run the Red in tomorra. I feel too good today, what with

Fungo about to score the tie-breaking run.

FOOTS FUNGO

(*scoring the tie-breaking run all the way from first on a single*)

I got a good jump on the hit-and-run sign and just kept goin'.

SEAN ALEXANDER KURKJIAN

His feet are fleet.

GENERAL KIDWELL

Miss Riaganoti and I will be married tomorrow in a simple military ceremony at second base between games of the doubleheader. I—I

(*He blushes.*)

—just like to *do* her!

SIGNORINA RIGATONI

Oh, Milk-ee! Do me now! Een front everybody, I no care. My eyes are blazink, no? No, no?

BARNACLE BILL

Don't get so sore and lay on the floor.

SIGNORINA RIGATONI

(*lying on the floor*)

You like thees pose, Milk-ee? You like? Aha! I see your medals begin glowink! With how you say the heat, no?

GENERAL KIDWELL

This is highly irregular, Miss Ragotiono, but—

(*He does her.*)

PETER BOFFO

Somehow, in its own dark, peculiar way, this is—*literature*!

VINNIE PACHISI

That fuckin' settles it! I'm gonna make my Easter Duty right fuckin' now!

FOOTS FUNGO

(*hitting a grand slam*)

I just tried to meet the ball and stay out of a double play.

SEAN ALEXANDER KURKJIAN

That shot was hot.

ALL

Was hot!

The Masquers now descend upon the stage to mingle with the other players and the Audience. The clouds and mist that enveloped them at the beginning of our entertainment are no more; there is now surrounding each glittering sunshine, and their snowy-clad figures are clear against a blue sky on which backdrop pennants snap in a cool breeze. Their uniforms, purest white, proclaim their changed names in letters of richly burnished gold. They are now, the pitcher, SPLENDOR, catcher, CLARITY, first baseman, GERMINATION, second baseman, JOY, third baseman, TEMPERANCE, shortstop, LOVELINESS, left fielder, MERIT, center fielder, PERFECTION, and right fielder, HARMONY. Their leader, HOPE, leads them in joyous galliards and corantos, which ALL then follow.

FATHER MAVOURNEEN
and
MONSIGNOR O'HARA

(*from Purgatory*)

Frail, jolly scene, bother of Jersey, our strife, our sleekness, and our trope! For thee do we try, dour vanished children, naive, for thee do we render our thighs, scorning and creeping in this alley of beers. Learn then, pugnacious celibates, kind sighs of calm seas, bear us; fond laughter dress our sex while dough comes to us; caressèd loot of shy bloom, seize us. No torment, no shoving, no cheating unwary.

JAMES JOYCE

Ere we hit the hay, brothers, let's have that response to prayer.

ALL

No cheating unwary.

JAMES JOYCE

Loud, heap miseries upon us yet entwine our arts with laughters low!

ALL

With laughters low!

Printed November 1974 in Santa Barbara & Ann Arbor for the Black Sparrow Press by Noel Young & Edwards Brothers Inc. Design by Barbara Martin. This edition is published in paper wrappers; there are 200 hardcover copies numbered & signed by the poet; & 26 copies handbound in boards by Earle Gray lettered & signed by the poet.

179

Photo: David Wyland

Gilbert Sorrentino was born in Brooklyn, New York in 1929. He attended the public schools and Brooklyn College, but did not graduate. From 1951 to 1953 he served in the Army Medical Corps. He was the editor of *Neon*, a literary magazine that appeared irregularly between 1956 and 1960. Subsequently, he was a member of the editorial staff of *Kulchur*, a New York-based magazine of comment and criticism, and for five years was an editor at Grove Press. He has written four books of poems, three novels, and a short work of fiction. In 1973-74 he was a Guggenheim Fellow. He lives in New York with his family, where he is at work on a long novel, of which *Flawless Play Restored* is a section.